Grammar Book

Linnette Erocak

Contents

I'm wearing a T-shirt

1 **Read the text. What's the weather like today?**

posted 3:15 p.m. ♥ 3 likes

Hi, it's me, Anita. Today is Saturday and I'm at home with my family. We can't go to the beach today because it's raining. I wear a sunhat and my blue swimsuit at the beach. Today I'm wearing jeans and a T-shirt.

My brother is playing with his cars. He's in his bedroom. When it's cold, he wears his favorite scarf and gloves. Today he's wearing shorts and a sweatshirt. It's warm in the house.

My dad is in the garden. He's fixing the shed. When it's sunny, he wears sandals and a baseball cap. Today he's wearing boots and his raincoat, but he's still getting wet! Poor Dad!

2 **Read and write T (*true*) or F (*false*).**

1   Anita's dad is wearing a cap.   ....

2   Anita is wearing her blue swimsuit.   ....

3   Her brother is in his bedroom.   ....

4   It's snowing today.   ....

5   Anita's dad is in the garden.   ....

Grammar

I wear a T-shirt when it's warm.	I'm wearing a T-shirt today.
It doesn't snow in summer.	It isn't snowing today.
Do you wear a swimsuit at the beach?	Are you wearing a swimsuit now?
Yes, we do.	No, we don't.	Yes, we are.	No, we aren't.

3 **Read the text again and underline sentences with *-ing*.**

4 Circle the correct answer.

1 It's *snow / snowing* today.

2 They're *wearing / wear* hats.

3 She *wears / wearing* boots in the rain.

4 It *doesn't rain / isn't raining* today.

5 Read the sentences and answer the questions.

1 Look! It's snowing!

2 It often snows in winter.

A Which sentence talks about an activity that happens regularly? ....

B Which sentence talks about an activity that is happening now? ....

6 Complete the sentences with the correct form of the word.

Oh, look! It **(1)** .... (rain). Putri loves rain. She always **(2)** .... (bring) her pink umbrella when it's raining. **(3)** .... she .... (wear) a jacket? No, she isn't. It's warm. She **(4)** .... (wear) a pink blouse today. It matches her umbrella!

7 Think of a type of weather and tell a friend what you are wearing. Your friend guesses the weather.

I'm wearing a T-shirt and shorts. I'm not wearing a coat.

Is it sunny?

Yes, it is.

8 📋 **Look at the pictures and read the questions. Write one-word answers.**

What's the weather like? It's ____snowing____ .

1 Where are they? They're in the _____ .

2 What color is the girl's coat? It's _____ .

3 What are the women doing? They're _____ .

4 What are the women wearing? They're wearing _____ .

5 What's the weather like? It's _____ .

1 Read the dialog. What are they talking about?

Aya: Excuse me. Can you tell me where the aquarium is?

Youssef: Sure. It's across from the hospital.

Aya: Do you mean the new hospital on West Street?

Youssef: Yes, that's right.

Aya: How do I get there?

Youssef: First, go down this road and turn left at the stoplight. Next, go straight on King Street. Then go right at the sports center.

Aya: Oh, I know the sports center! My dad goes there sometimes.

Youssef: The aquarium isn't far from there. It's on the corner between the shopping mall and the movie theater.

Aya: How far is it from here?

Youssef: It's about a twenty-minute walk.

Aya: OK, thank you.

Youssef: No problem.

2 Read and write T (*true*) or F (*false*).

1 The aquarium is between the hospital and the sports center. ....

2 The aquarium is a twenty-minute walk from the sports center. ....

3 First, Aya needs to turn right at the stoplight. ....

4 The aquarium is on North Street. ....

5 The aquarium is across from the hospital. ....

3 Read the dialog again and underline sentences with *first*, *then*, and *next*.

Grammar

First, go straight on/go down/go along West Street.

Next, go right/turn right at the sports center.

Then go left/turn left at the stoplight.

4 Write the correct letter.

1 First, turn left onto Leaf Street. ....

2 Next, turn right onto James drive. ....

3 Then go to the corner of Green Street and Palmira Street. ....

4 My house is next to the bus stop. ....

A  B

C D

7

5 💡 Put the words in order.

1 Main Street down go First,

....

2 onto Grand Street left turn Then

....

3 corner on It's the of Grand Street James Street and

....

6 Look at the map and complete Eddie's description with one or two words.

Hi! I'm Eddie and this is my neighborhood. The school is close to my home. **(1)** .... , go along Grand Street. Then **(2)** .... onto Back Road. The school is on the left. I usually practice karate after school. The gym isn't very far. First, **(3)** .... onto Grand Street. **(4)** .... , turn left onto Short Street. Then **(5)** .... onto 5th Avenue. The gym is on the right.

7 ✏️ Draw a street map of your neighborhood. Write sentences giving directions to different places.

....
....
....
....
....
....
....

3 I rarely play basketball

1 Read the dialog. What sports and activities do Haruto and Dominik do?

Haruto: Hi, Dominik. Would you like to play basketball?

Dominik: Yes, I would. I love playing basketball!

Haruto: How often do you play?

Dominik: I usually play on the weekend. How about you?

Haruto: I rarely play basketball, but I often play soccer with my father. What else do you do in your free time?

Dominik: I usually go skateboarding with my brother in the evening. I sometimes ride my bike after school, and I always play tennis on Tuesdays.

Haruto: Do you like hockey?

Dominik: I don't know how to play.

Haruto: Really? Maybe I can teach you. I usually play hockey with some friends at the sports center.

Dominik: Sounds great.

Haruto: Let's go! The basketball game is about to start.

2 Read and circle T (*true*) or F (*false*).

1 Haruto rarely plays soccer.   T / F
2 Haruto never plays basketball.   T / F
3 Dominik usually plays basketball on the weekend.   T / F
4 Dominik usually goes skateboarding with his brother.   T / F

3 Read the dialog again and underline the frequency words.

4 Look at the chart and circle the correct answer.

	play the piano	do karate	play table tennis	ride a bike
Ivan	✓✓	✓✓✓		✓
Jelena	✓✓✓✓		✓✓✓✓✓	✓

1 Jelena *always / rarely* plays table tennis.

2 Ivan *sometimes / usually* plays the piano.

3 Ivan *never / often* does karate.

4 Jelena *rarely / never* rides her bike.

5 Read the sentences. Where do the frequency words go in questions and negative sentences?

1 I don't always go skateboarding on Saturdays.

2 Do you sometimes play hockey at school?

6 Put the words in order. You have to change some words.

1 do   brother   gymnastics   never   My

....

2 not   play   baseball   do   usually   Tom   on   Fridays

....

3 sometimes   with   her   play   friends   basketball   Paula

....

4 do   you   How   the   play   violin   often

.... ?

7 Complete the chart for yourself with the frequency words. Then ask a friend and complete.

How often do you play the piano?

I sometimes play the piano.

	Me	....
play the piano		
go skateboarding		
ride a bike		
do gymnastics		

4 How about going to the park?

1 Read the dialog. Where is Fatima?

Ahmed: Hi, Sofia. It's Ahmed.

Sofia: Hi, Ahmed!

Ahmed: Hey, let's do something this afternoon. How about going to the park?

Sofia: Sounds great, but I have a dentist appointment. Why don't we go tomorrow?

Ahmed: OK, good idea.

Sofia: Let's ask Fatima to come with us.

Ahmed: She's visiting her grandma this week.

Sofia: No, she isn't. She's at my house right now!

Ahmed: Oh! Can I talk to her, please?

Sofia: Sure, just a minute.

Fatima: Hi, Ahmed!

Ahmed: Hi, Fatima! I'd like to invite you to go to the park tomorrow with Sofia and me.

Fatima: Sorry, I can't. I'm going to the library.

Ahmed: Too bad. Well, how about going to the movie theater this evening?

Fatima: Sounds great!

Ahmed: OK! Can we meet at five o'clock?

Fatima: Sure, see you then.

2 Who said this? Write the correct name.

1 Can we meet at five o'clock? ....

2 Why don't we go tomorrow? ....

3 I'm going to the library. ....

4 Let's do something this afternoon. ....

3 Read the dialog again and underline the suggestion phrases.

Grammar

Let's go to the museum.

Why don't we go for a walk?

How about going to the movie theater?

Can we meet tomorrow?

I'd like to invite you to my birthday party.

4 Circle the correct answer.

1 Why don't *go / we go* to the swimming pool in the afternoon?

2 How about *watch / watching* a movie tonight?

3 Let's *go / going* to the movie theater!

4 I'd like to *invite / inviting* Jane to the park.

5 Read the sentences. What is different about the sentence with *how about*?

1 Let's meet at one o'clock.

2 Why don't we play baseball?

3 How about playing table tennis?

4 I'd like to go skateboarding.

6 Complete the sentences.

1

.... don't we go swimming this afternoon?

2

.... go to the movie theater on Wednesday evening!

3

I'd .... invite you to my house this weekend.

4

.... playing basketball after school?

7 You invited your friend to visit you. Decide what you would like to do. Talk about what you'd like to eat for lunch.

Student A

- You'd like to go swimming or play hide and seek. You don't have badminton rackets.

- You don't like chicken. You like pizza and hot dogs.

Student B

- You can't swim. You'd like to play badminton or hide and seek.

- You don't like hot dogs. You like chicken and pizza.

Why don't we go swimming?

I can't swim, sorry. How about playing badminton?

I don't have badminton rackets. I know! Let's...

My family moved to a new city

1 Read the text. What happened to Carlos on the first day of school?

Hi, I'm Carlos. Last year, my family moved to a new city. Summer was over and it was the first day of school. I was very nervous. My new school is very close to our house, so I walked there. The weather wasn't cold so there were a lot of students outside the school on the grass. I was the new boy, so everyone looked at me. I walked towards the door, but I didn't notice the big rock on the ground. I tripped over it and dropped all my books! Some people pointed and laughed. I wanted to cry, but then a group of kids walked over to me. They smiled and helped me pick up my books. I was so happy. I thanked them and we started talking. Now we are all best friends.

2 Read and circle T (*true*) or F (*false*).

1. When Carlos arrived at school, everybody looked at him.   T / F

2. Carlos was very nervous on the first day of school.   T / F

3. Carlos lives close to school.   T / F

4. The weather was very cold.   T / F

Grammar

I/He/She/It was cold.	I/He/She/It wasn't cold.
We/You/They were late.	We/You/They weren't late.
Were you tired?	Yes, I was. No, I wasn't.
I/He/She/It moved to Caracas.	I/He/She/It didn't move to Caracas.
We/You/They walked to school.	We/You/They didn't walk to school.
Did you laugh?	Yes, I did. No, I didn't.

3 Read the text again and underline action words in the past.

4 Circle the correct answer.

1. Ada *wasn't danced / didn't dance* last night.

2. My father *finished / was finish* his work at five.

3. Hamza *didn't / not* like the movie we watched.

4. Selma and her sister *not late / weren't late* for school.

5

Which words behave the same? Color the action words blue, yellow, or green.

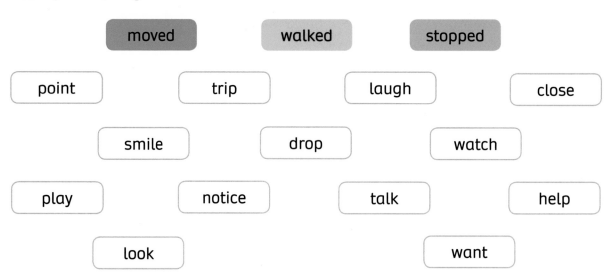

moved   walked   stopped

point   trip   laugh   close

smile   drop   watch

play   notice   talk   help

look   want

6

Complete the text with the correct form of the words.

posted 11:35 a.m.   4 likes

My last birthday **(1)** _____ (be) amazing. My mom **(2)** _____ (invite) all my friends to our beach house. It was a very warm day. We **(3)** _____ (play) volleyball. Two of my friends **(4)** _____ (stay) for the night. We **(5)** _____ (watch) a movie and played video games. It was fun!

7

Write about your last birthday. Where was it? Who did you invite? What was the weather like? Use Activity 6 to help you.

....

....

....

....

....

....

We sang songs around the campfire

1 **Read the text. What did Tavit do last weekend?**

Last weekend, our teacher took our class on a field trip. We went camping in Fremond State Park. We chose all the activities two weeks ago. First, we went hiking around the hills. Then we made a campfire and ate hot dogs for lunch. In the evening, the forest was very quiet. We sang songs around the campfire then went to bed. In the morning, I woke up early and had some eggs and toast. After breakfast, we went for a walk around the forest. We saw a lot of interesting plants and insects. Then our teacher took us on a rafting trip down the river. We were all exhausted at the end of the day! It was a great trip. I can't wait for next year!

2 **Read and write _Yes_ or _No_.**

1 In the evening, the forest was very noisy. ....

2 First, they made a campfire. ....

3 Tavit went camping last weekend.

    ....

4 Tavit woke up early. ....

5 Tavit didn't enjoy the class trip this year. ....

3 **Read the text again and underline action words in the past.**

4 **Circle the correct answer.**

1 A: _Do / Did_ they watch the fireworks yesterday?

    B: No, they _don't / didn't_.

2 A: When did you _do / did_ your homework?

    B: I _do / did_ it on Monday.

3 A: Is that your new skateboard?

    B: Yes, my dad _buy / bought_ it three days ago.

4 A: Did you _sleep / slept_ well last night?

    B: Yes, I did. What _do / did_ you _do / did_ last night?

    A: I _eat / ate_ out with my family.

Grammar

I/You woke up early last weekend.	I/You didn't wake up early last weekend.
He/She/It went camping a week ago.	He/She/It didn't go camping a week ago.
We/You/They sang songs yesterday.	We/You/They didn't sing songs yesterday.
Did you see any interesting plants?	Yes, I did. No, I didn't.

5 💡 Which time expressions can be used in the past? Circle them.

on Saturdays   two weeks ago   last month   always

every day   now   in 2005

tomorrow   yesterday   last year

6 Complete the sentences with the correct words.

had   yesterday   went   ate   ago   didn't swim   last

1   I didn't take any photos ....
2   Did you go camping .... week?
3   I .... yesterday. I forgot my swimsuit!
4   She went camping three months ....
5   We .... to the aquarium for my birthday.
6   We .... a lot of fun last Sunday.
7   She .... all the pizza! I didn't have any.

7 💬 Ask a friend about his or her last summer vacation.

What did you do last summer?

I went to a beach resort.

Sounds great! Did you swim in the ocean?

8 Look at the pictures and read the questions. Write one-word answers.

What did the children do on Friday morning?
They _____got_____ on the bus.

1 Where did they go? They .... on a field trip.

2 What place did they visit? They .... an aquarium.
3 What did the boy see there? He .... colorful fish.

4 What did the boy draw? He .... a fish.
5 Did he have fun at the aquarium? Yes, he ....

17

7 Did you read the book?

1 Read the dialog. What happened to the duckling in the end?

Mom: It's time for dinner. Did you finish your homework?

Ona: Yes, I did. I read a fairy tale called *The Ugly Duckling.*

Mom: Did you enjoy the story?

Ona: Yes, I did. It was about a sad little duckling.

Mom: Why was he unhappy?

Ona: Because he was different from the other ducklings.

Mom: That's so sad! What did he do?

Ona: One day he left home.

Mom: Oh, dear. What happened next?

Ona: A farmer found him.

Mom: Where did he take him?

Ona: He took him to his farm. In time, he grew bigger. One day he saw his reflection in a pond. He was beautiful and white. There were a lot of others just like him in the pond. He wasn't a duck at all! He was a swan!

Mom: Was he happy?

Ona: Oh, yes! He made friends with the other swans and lived happily ever after.

2 Read and answer the questions.

1 Who found the duckling?
2 Was the duckling sad at the end?
3 Did Ona like the story?
4 What's the title of the story?

3 Read the dialog again and underline the questions.

Grammar

Did you read the book?

Was she happy?

Where did he take him?

Why did she do that?

What was his name?

When was the party?

4 Choose the correct answer.

1 Why .... he unhappy?

   A be   B were   C was

2 .... the farmer take the duckling?

   A Is   B Did   C Was

3 Did he .... friends with the other children?

   A make   B making   C made

4 What .... they do?

   A are   B did   C were

5 .... was the farm?

   A When   B Why   C Where

6 .... the story sad?

   A Was   B Were   C When

18

5 Put the words in order. What is different about sentence two?

duckling   Was   the   sad

1 .... ?

was   duckling   sad   the   Why

2 .... ?

6 Complete the questions with the correct words.

Was   read   leave   did   enjoy   did   Did

1 When .... Ona .... the story?

2 .... she .... the story?

3 Why .... the duckling .... home?

4 .... the duckling beautiful?

7 Choose a fairy tale from the pictures below. Your friend asks questions and guesses the fairy tale.

Puss in Boots

The Little Mermaid

Little Red Riding Hood

What was the story about?

It was about a princess.

Where did she live?

8 Look at the pictures, read the story, and complete the sentences.

One day, a princess dropped her favorite golden ball in a pond. She was very sad.

But a frog said, "I can find your golden ball, but you have to give me something I want." The princess agreed and the frog found her ball. The princess was very happy.

1 Why _____ the princess sad? Because she lost her ball.

2 What _____ the frog do? He _____ her ball.

The next morning, the frog came to the palace. It said, "I want to live with you." The princess was unhappy about this. She didn't want to live with the frog. But she had to keep her promise. The frog lived in the palace with the princess.

3 When _____ the frog arrive at the palace? It _____ the next morning.

4 What _____ the frog want? It _____ to live in the palace.

5 What _____ the princess _____? She _____ her promise.

One day, the princess kissed the frog goodnight. It turned into a handsome prince! He told the princess about the witch who turned him into a frog. The princess and the prince married and lived happily ever after.

6 What _____ the witch turn the prince into? She _____ him into a frog.

7 What did the frog become? He _____ a handsome prince.

20

1 Take the quiz with a friend.

1 Which animal is the fastest on land?

A   a cheetah   B   a lion
C   an elephant

2 Which animal is taller?

A   a giraffe   B   a gorilla

3 Which animal is the slowest?

A   a zebra   B   a tortoise
C   a tiger

4 Which animal is bigger than a snake?

A   a frog   B   a crocodile

5 Which animal is the biggest on Earth?

A   a bear   B   a koala
C   a blue whale

6 Which animal is the largest?

A   a hippo   B   a lion
C   a panda

7 Which animal is the strongest?

A   a gazelle   B   a snake
C   a gorilla

8 Which animal is shorter than a kangaroo?

A   a koala   B   an elephant
C   a giraffe

9 Which animal is the heaviest on land?

A   a bear   B   an elephant
C   a tiger

10 Which animal is the fastest in water?

A   a crocodile   B   a blue shark
C   a turtle

2 Read and write *Yes* or *No*.

1 A crocodile is smaller than a snake.

....

2 A blue whale is the biggest animal on Earth. ....

3 A gorilla is stronger than a gazelle.

....

4 An elephant is the heaviest animal on land. ....

3 Read the quiz again. Underline words that end in *-er* in blue and words that end in *-est* in red.

Grammar

A giraffe is tall. A giraffe is taller than a horse. A giraffe is the tallest animal!

A bear is big. A bear is bigger than a tiger. A bear is the biggest animal in our zoo.

A cat is friendly. A cat is friendlier than a crocodile. A cat is the friendliest animal.

A panda is cute. A panda is cuter than an elephant. A panda is the cutest animal.

4 Circle the correct answer.

1 A tiger is *stronger / strongest* than a giraffe.

2 Blue whales are *biggest / the biggest* animals on Earth.

3 Snakes are *the longer / longer* than lizards.

4 A sloth is the *lazy / laziest* animal of all.

5 What is missing? Write.

-gest -er -ier

1 Crocodiles are long .... than lizards.

2 A panda is friendl .... than a tiger.

3 Blue whales are the big .... animals.

6 Put the words in order.

1 longer Snakes lizards than are

....

2 are Pandas than lions friendlier

....

3 tallest Giraffes animals the are Earth on

....

4 is land cheetah fastest on A the animal

....

7 Take turns comparing the koala, cheetah, and elephant. Use the words in the box to help you.

big tall short strong fast lazy small

A koala is smaller than an elephant.

A cheetah is faster than an elephant.

A cheetah is bigger than a koala.

8 **Look at the pictures and read. Write the correct words on the lines.**

a snake

a panda

a blue whale

an elephant

a gorilla

a giraffe

This is the biggest animal in the world. It lives in the ocean. a blue whale

1 This animal is taller than an elephant. It eats leaves and grass. ....

2 This animal is from China and eats bamboo. It's smaller than a polar bear.

....

3 This animal doesn't have legs or arms. It's longer than a lizard. ....

4 This animal has large ears. It's the heaviest animal on land. ....

5 This animal is from Africa. It's bigger than a panda. It eats leaves and plants.

....

1 **Read the text. What does Aljaz enjoy doing the most?**

Hello there! I'm Aljaz. I have a lot of hobbies. During the week, I play soccer, tennis, and basketball with my friends. I think basketball is the most energetic, because you have to jump! On the weekend, I like skateboarding. I think skateboarding is more exciting than playing basketball. I sometimes ride my bike when the weather is nice. Riding a bike is more difficult when it's cold and wet. In winter, model making is the most practical hobby. My dad and I make models of old ships, but I find collecting coins more interesting. I have a lot of different coins. I keep the most valuable coins in a special box. I'm also learning to play chess. Playing chess with my family is more enjoyable than everything else!

2 **Read and write T (*true*) or F (*false*).**

1   Aljaz has many hobbies. ....

2   He thinks soccer is the most energetic sport. ....

3   He finds collecting coins more interesting than model making. ....

4   He keeps his models in a special box. ....

3 **Read the text again and underline describing words with *more* and *the most*.**

Grammar

Tennis is exciting. Soccer is more exciting than tennis. But basketball is the most exciting sport.

Drawing is relaxing. Reading is more relaxing than drawing. Riding my bike is the most relaxing hobby.

Painting is interesting. Collecting coins is more interesting than painting. Model making is the most interesting.

4 **Circle the correct answer.**

1   Reading is *relaxing / more relaxing* than playing chess.

2   Skateboarding is the *most dangerous / more dangerous* sport.

3   I think collecting stamps is *more exciting / the most exciting* than collecting coins.

4   Swimming is *most enjoyable / more enjoyable* than playing soccer.

5 💡 What is different about the sentences?

1 Skateboarding is easier than riding a bike.

2 Playing chess is more challenging than playing video games.

6 Complete the sentences with the correct form of the word.

1 Doing karate is _____ (exciting) than doing gymnastics.

2 Collecting coins is _____ (interesting) hobby for me.

3 Skateboarding is _____ (dangerous) outdoor activity.

4 I think model making is _____ (enjoyable) reading.

5 Playing chess is _____ (challenging) painting.

6 Reading is _____ (relaxing) hobby for me.

7 💬 Work in pairs. Ask and answer questions with a friend about free time activities.

| playing chess | riding a bike | reading | horseback riding |

| playing badminton | playing video games | collecting stamps |

| soccer | painting | playing volleyball | collecting coins |

Which activity is more interesting, collecting stamps or coins?

I think collecting stamps is more interesting than collecting coins.

Which sport do you think is the most exciting, badminton, soccer or volleyball?

I think soccer is the most exciting sport.

8 Read the story. Choose the right words and write them on the lines.

Juan thinks that riding a bike is ____*the*____ most exciting hobby.
He got a new bike for his birthday. He went for a bike ride with his
friends in the park. The park is a **(1)** _____ place to ride
bikes than the street. Riding down a hill is **(2)** _____
dangerous than riding on flat ground, but Juan wanted to go fast! So
he and his friends rode to the top of **(3)** _____ hill they
could find. It was more **(4)** _____ than riding on flat
ground. Juan rode down first. He went too fast and couldn't turn. He
rode straight into a bush! That was the **(5)** _____ bike ride
in his whole life!

	(the)	a	than
1	safe	safer	safest
2	more	most	the
3	tallest	taller	the tallest
4	exhaustinger	exhausting	exhaustingest
5	scarier	most scarier	scariest

We don't have any bottled water

1 **Read the note. What does Oscar's mom want him to do?**

Hi, Oscar!

I'm working late tonight and I don't have time to go to the store. Can you please go to the store with your sister and buy the things on this list for our picnic tomorrow? I left some money for you next to the microwave.

- We need some apples and some oranges.
- I know you don't like orange juice, so please buy some lemonade.
- Is there any cheese left? Please check and buy some if we need it.
- We need some chips. You can buy your favorite kind!
- We don't have any bottled water. Please buy some.
- Can you buy some pasta, too? I want to make a pasta salad.

That's all, but if you think of anything else you want for the picnic, call me. You can ask your sister to stop for some ice cream on the way home. See you later tonight!

Love,

Mom

2 **Read and circle T (*true*) or F (*false*).**

1 Mom left some money in the microwave. T / F

2 Oscar likes orange juice. T / F

3 There isn't any bottled water. T / F

4 Mom wants some pasta. T / F

Grammar

I have some rice and some pasta.

I don't have any water or any soup.

Can you buy some cereal?

Are there any apples in the basket?

3 **Read the note again and underline sentences with *some* in blue and *any* in orange.**

4 **Circle the correct answer.**

1 There isn't *some / any* water in the bottle.

2 There are *some / any* mushrooms.

3 There is *some / any* orange juice.

4 There aren't *some / any* carrots in the basket.

5 Look at the sentences. When do we use *some* in questions? When do we use *any* in questions?

1 Can you buy some apples? Yes, of course.

2 Would you like some chocolate? Yes, please.

3 Is there any milk in the fridge? Yes, there is.

4 Are there any oranges? No, there aren't.

6 Complete the sentences with *some* or *any*.

1 There are .... carrots on the table.

2 We don't have .... yogurt.

3 Is there .... chicken on the pizza?

4 There is .... tomato sauce in the pan.

5 There isn't .... pasta in the pantry.

6 Would you like .... sugar in your tea?

7 Draw some food in your fridge. Then write what's in your fridge.

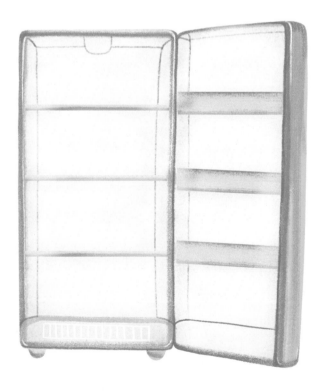

There is some apple juice in the fridge.

There aren't any oranges in the fridge.

1 Read the dialog. Which animal does Aylin like the most?

Adria: Hello, Aylin. What are you up to?

Aylin: Hi, Adria! I'm going to the zoo after school. I'm so excited!

Adria: That sounds amazing! Which animal do you like the most?

Aylin: Crocodiles. I like tigers, too, but crocodiles are more interesting than tigers. What about you?

Adria: I think cheetahs are the most fascinating animals because they are faster than any other animal.

Aylin: I heard there are cheetahs at the zoo, too. Why don't we go together?

Adria: I would love to, but I have to finish my project for school tomorrow. How about playing basketball tomorrow after school?

Aylin: That sounds great. I usually play basketball with Jeremy on Sundays.

Adria: Where do you usually play?

Aylin: We play at the courts on West Street. Do you know where that is?

Adria: No. Can you tell me how to get to West Street from here?

Aylin: Sure. First, go straight on East Street. Next, go right at the museum. The basketball courts are next to the shopping mall.

Adria: Great! See you there tomorrow.

2 Read and write T (*true*) or F (*false*).

1 Aylin finds crocodiles more interesting than tigers. ....

2 There aren't any cheetahs in the zoo. ....

3 Adria is going to the zoo with Aylin. ....

4 Aylin plays basketball with Jeremy. ....

3 Read the dialog again and write an example sentence from the text.

Giving directions: ....

Comparing two things: ....

An invitation: ....

4 Match to make sentences.

1 How about
2 Tigers have longer tails
3 Let's
4 Blue whales are

A the biggest animals in the world.
B go to the zoo.
C than dogs.
D going to the lake?

5 Complete the sentences with the correct words.

isn't   any   there   have   some   is

1 There _____ some lemonade.
2 We don't have _____ tomatoes.
3 Are _____ any bananas?
4 There are _____ cookies.
5 We _____ some apples.
6 There _____ any soup.

6 Put the words in order.

1 tennis   play   We   week   every

....

2 the   at   moment   horse   riding   She   a   is

....

3 evening   never   I   violin   practice   the   the   in

....

4 for   mom   My   cooking   stew   isn't   dinner

....

7 Read the answers and write the questions.

1 ....?

Simon's the tallest in our class.

2 ....?

I visited my cousin last weekend.

3 ....?

The nearest bus stop is on West Street.

8 **Read the text and choose the best answer.**

Alina: Hi, Ion. Where are you going?

Ion: (A) I'm going to basketball practice.

B They're going home.

C Where's this?

1 **Alina:** How often do you play basketball?

Ion: A The field is on King Street.

B Twice a week, on Mondays and Wednesdays.

C Why don't we go this evening?

2 **Alina:** Is P.E. your favorite subject?

Ion: A Yes, I am.

B I often go.

C No, I only like basketball.

3 **Alina:** Do you like science?

Ion: A Yes, it's more interesting than math.

B Not much, we're going swimming.

C We are going camping.

4 **Alina:** Why don't we do our science project together?

Ion: A That sounds great.

B Because it isn't interesting.

C I usually play basketball on the weekends.

5 **Alina:** Can we meet on Saturday?

Ion: A I'm not playing.

B Yes, it's rainy.

C Monday is better for me.

6 **Alina:** Great! Where can we meet?

Ion: A It's next to the train station.

B At the library.

C At 2 p.m.

12 I had a can of soda

1 Read the review of the school cafeteria. Was the food tasty?

New cafeteria now open!

Hi! This is Amanda. Today I'm writing about the new cafeteria at our school. It's very colorful and modern. There's a lot of space for all the students. There are a lot of interesting snacks, drinks, and desserts. The prices are very reasonable, too. You can buy a bag of chips, a bar of chocolate or a piece of fruit for a quick snack. For lunch you can have a slice of pizza, a bowl of salad, or a sandwich. I had a slice of pizza and a can of soda. My friend, Jackie, had a ham sandwich and a glass of milk. There are many different cakes for dessert. It was difficult to choose just one! I had a piece of chocolate cake. Jackie had a piece of carrot cake. All the food was delicious.

The new cafeteria is great. There's usually a very long line, but it's worth the wait!

2 Read and write T (*true*) or F (*false*).

1 Jackie had a glass of milk. ....

2 You can't buy any fruit. ....

3 There are a lot of interesting snacks on the menu. ....

4 Jackie had a cupcake. ....

3 Read the review again and underline the food phrases.

4 Look and circle the correct answer.

1 a bag of chips /
a can of chips

2 a cup of milk /
a bottle of milk

3 a piece of cake /
a box of cake

4 a can of soda /
a bottle of soda

5 a bottle of chocolates /
a box of chocolates

Grammar

a can of soda, two cans of soda

a glass of milk, two glasses of milk

a cup of tea, two cups of tea

a bottle of water, two bottles of water

a slice of pizza, two slices of pizza

a bag of chips, two bags of chips

a piece of cake, two pieces of cake

a loaf of bread, two loaves of bread

a bowl of cereal, two bowls of cereal

5 What is missing? Write two things for each.

chips   soda   cola   pizza   water   bread   cookies   milk

1   a bottle of .... , ...

2   a can of .... , ...

3   a slice of .... , ...

4   a bag of .... , ...

6 Complete the sentences with the correct phrases.

two cans of   a cup of   a bar of   a bottle of   two bags of   a piece of

1   I have .... water in my bag.

2   Ann drank .... hot chocolate in the cafeteria.

3   Suzy and I ate .... chips after school.

4   My father had .... cake on his birthday.

5   Sandy bought .... chocolate for me!

6   Carla drinks .... soda every day.

7 Do a class survey. What did you eat and drink yesterday? Ask and answer with friends.

Name	water	milk	cake	chips	soda	pizza

Did you drink any water yesterday?

Yes, I drank three glasses of water.

Did you have any cake?

No, I didn't. But I had a slice of pizza!

1 **Read the descriptions. Which animal can only be found in Africa?**

Crocodiles live in large shallow tropical lakes and rivers in Africa, Asia, Australia, and the Americas. They are carnivores. This means they only eat meat. Crocodiles have massive long bodies. A crocodile has about seventy big sharp teeth in its mouth. They can swim very fast and they can run fast on land, too.

Cheetahs live in dry open grasslands in Africa. They are identified by the small round black spots on their yellow fur. Cheetahs have long slender muscular bodies. They can run very fast because they have four long strong legs. In fact, they are the fastest mammals on land. Cheetahs are carnivores.

Elephants live in hot tropical grasslands in the African Savanna. Some elephants also live in tropical evergreen forests in Asia. Each elephant has a long gray trunk and two large floppy ears. Elephants are one of the largest land animals. They have two long curved tusks. Elephants only eat plants, because they are herbivores.

2 **Complete the sentences with the missing word.**

1 Elephants have long gray

....

2 Cheetahs have small round
.... on their body.

3 Crocodiles .... swim very fast.

4 Elephants have .... long curved tusks.

Grammar

Elephants have long gray trunks.

Cheetahs have small round black spots.

Crocodiles have seventy big sharp teeth.

3 **Read the text again and underline the describing words.**

4 **Circle the correct answer.**

1 Tigers have *long black / black long* stripes on their bodies.

2 Giraffes have *slender long / long slender* necks.

3 Crocodiles have *strong four / four strong* legs.

4 My cat has a *soft long striped / long striped soft* tail.

5 We adopted a *friendly small black / black friendly small* puppy.

5 Put the words in order.

1 have   fluffy   Rabbits   fur   brown   short

....

2 sharp   have   teeth   big   Crocodiles   seventy

....

6 Put describing words in the correct order and complete the sentences.

1 Pandas have .... eyes.

2 Tigers have .... fur.

3 Zebras have .... legs.

round   black   small

orange   beautiful   short

thin   four   striped

7 Choose an animal from the pictures below and describe it to your friend. Your friend guesses the animal.

This animal has a long gray body.

Is it a dolphin?

Yes, it is!

Is anyone interested in Egypt?

1 **Read the texts. What does each student need?**

Hi everybody! I'm very nervous about going to school. My project is due tomorrow, but it isn't finished. I'm afraid of getting the facts wrong. I need help! Is anyone interested in Egypt? Where can I find information about the pyramids?

— Marcos, 11

Hello there! Today was my first day at my new school. I was so excited about making new friends. I was surprised by everyone's warm welcome. My problem is that I am confused about my geography homework. Can anyone lend me an atlas? I really need some help!

— Clara, 12

Hello! My friend and I are preparing a project about recycling and we're really excited about it. Our teachers are really happy with our work, but we need more students to help. Is anyone interested in helping us?

— Aleix, 12

Hi. I'm shocked by the homework my teacher gave us! It's very long and difficult. I'm trying to do it now, but I can't. I'm kind of stressed about it. Can someone tell me how to write a composition, please?

— Amelia, 13

2 **Read and write the names.**

1 Who is nervous about his/her project? ....

2 Who is stressed about the homework? ....

3 Who is excited about his/her project? ....

4 Who was surprised by a warm welcome? ....

Grammar

He is tired of doing his homework.

They are interested in helping others.

Clara was surprised by the warm welcome!

She was excited about her new bike.

Our teacher was happy with our project.

He is nervous about the interview.

We were confused by our homework.

My mom is stressed about her new job.

Emma is afraid of spiders.

The teacher was shocked by Tim's behavior.

I am bored with this TV show.

3 **Read the text again and underline the feeling phrases.**

4 **Look at the pictures and circle the correct answer.**

1 She is *nervous about / happy with* doing her homework.

2 Mihai is *bored with / shocked by* the scary movie.

3 He is *excited about / confused by* the question.

4 Ioana was *excited about / tired of* news of the school trip.

5 **Which words go together? Match.**

stressed

happy

confused

nervous

by

shocked

about

with

excited

bored

surprised

6 **Complete the sentences with the correct word.**

1 I was surprised .... my birthday present.

2 He's afraid .... snakes.

3 She's bored .... all her toys.

4 They're interested .... recycling.

5 I'm nervous .... my exam.

7 **Ask a friend questions about his or her feelings.**

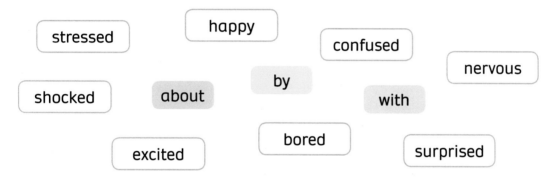

What are you excited about?

I'm excited about my vacation.

8 **Look at the pictures and read. Write _Yes_ or _No_.**

1   She is tired of cleaning her room. ....

2   He is surprised by his gift.

....

3   They are afraid of playing in the snow. ....

4   Ali is happy with his test. ....

5   Leonora is excited about her visit at the dentist's office. ....

Why do you like spring the most?

1 **Read the dialog. Why does the teacher like all seasons?**

Teacher: Today we are talking about the seasons. Now tell me, what is your favorite season and why?

Paola: I like summer because I like riding my bike with my friends. I also love swimming in the ocean.

Ana: I like winter because I like playing in the snow!

Teacher: What about you, Diego?

Diego: My favorite season is spring.

Teacher: Why do you like spring the most?

Diego: I like it because I start volleyball practice in spring!

Teacher: Very nice. And Abdel? Do you like spring, too?

Abdel: No, I don't.

Teacher: Why not?

Abdel: I like flying my kite and there isn't enough wind to fly my kite in spring! The weather is perfect in fall for flying kites, so I like fall the best.

Teacher: Selim, which season do you like?

Selim: I love spring because the grass is so green! There are flowers everywhere. What is your favorite season, Ms. Greystone?

Teacher: I like all seasons because I like playing table tennis! I can play table tennis in any weather!

2 **Read and write T (*true*) or F (*false*).**

1 Paola likes summer because she likes swimming. ....

2 Diego likes spring because he has soccer practice. ....

3 Abdel doesn't like spring because there isn't enough wind for flying kites. ....

4 Selim likes winter because the air is so fresh. ....

Grammar

Why do you like fall?
I like fall because I can fly my kite.

Mert's wearing boots because it's raining outside.

She can't go to school because she's sick.

3 **Read the dialog again and underline questions with *why* in green. Underline sentences with *because* in purple.**

4 **Choose the correct answer.**

1 I like summer

   A because I like swimming.

   B because I can play in the snow.

2 We aren't riding our bikes

   A because it didn't rain today.

   B because it's raining.

3 He's wearing his boots

   A because it's snowy.

   B because I like skateboarding.

5 💡 **Complete the sentences with *why* or *because*. When do we use *why*? When do we use *because*?**

1   A: _____ do you like Tom?

    B: I like him _____ he's very funny.

2   A: _____ are you wearing sunglasses?

    B: I'm wearing sunglasses _____ it's sunny.

6 **Read the answers and write the questions.**

1   _____ ?

    I like winter because I like skiing.

2   _____ ?

    I'm running because I'm late.

3   _____ ?

    I'm wearing a sweatshirt because it's cold.

7 💬 **Look at the pictures. Ask and answer with a friend about why you like or don't like each sport.**

Why do you like basketball?

I like basketball because I can run fast.

8 Look at the pictures and read the story. Write some words to complete the sentences about the story. You can use 1, 2, or 3 words.

This was the best summer vacation ever because Zehra went to the beach with her family. She loves swimming in the cool water when it's hot outside. Her brother wasn't happy because he broke his arm last week. He couldn't swim in the ocean with his sister. He couldn't play volleyball with his dad. Zehra wanted to make her brother happy. She knew he really liked board games. So in the evenings, they played board games together. This made him happy again.

1 Zehra was happy because she went ....

2 Zehra's brother was .... because he couldn't swim in the ocean.

3 They played board games in the evenings .... Zehra's brother likes doing this.

Alex likes windy days because he loves flying his kite. On Saturday morning, Alex woke up and looked out of his bedroom window. The sky was gray and cloudy. He opened the window and felt the wind on his face. He was very excited. He ran downstairs and took his kite out of the closet. He put on his jacket because it was cold outside. The wind blew hard. The weather was perfect. His kite flew high in the sky!

4 Alex likes .... because he can fly his kite then.

5 The sky was .... on Saturday.

6 Alex ran downstairs because he was ....

7 The weather was perfect for flying kites because the ....

1 Read the emails. What will Aleyna and Jennifer celebrate?

Dear Youssef,

My birthday is on January 29, so on Saturday I would like to celebrate it with all my friends! My mother promised to make a big chocolate cake with nine candles on it. I would like a new bike for my birthday! I hope my parents buy me one. Yesterday my father bought lots of balloons for the party. I would like to invite all my friends and I'd like you to join us! Would you like to come to my party?

Your friend,

Aleyna

Dear Eva,

I'm very excited about our graduation next month! My mom bought me a pretty red dress. My dad bought a camera to take pictures of the ceremony. I would like some new shoes to wear with my dress! What about you? Are you ready for the big day?

After the ceremony, I would like to have dinner with my family and friends at my favorite Italian restaurant. I will book a big table!

Love,

Jennifer

2 Read and write T (*true*) or F (*false*).

1 Aleyna would like to celebrate her birthday with her sister. ....

2 She is eleven years old. ....

3 Jennifer is graduating next month. ....

4 She would like to have dinner alone after the ceremony. ....

Grammar

I would like to celebrate my birthday with my friends.

He would like to play chess with his friend this weekend.

She would like pizza for dinner.

We would like a new computer for our classroom.

3 Read the emails again and underline sentences with *would like*.

4 Match to make sentences.

1 Judy would like   A   meet you for dinner.

2 They would   B   a computer.

3 I would like to   C   like to celebrate their birthday.

5 Complete the sentences.

would like   would like to

1 Daniel _____ blow out the candles.
2 We _____ a new computer for Christmas.

6 Look at the pictures and complete the sentences.

1 I would _____ a _____ for lunch.
2 Sam _____ to _____
to the _____ .
3 Jenny _____ a pink
_____ for her birthday.
4 We _____
celebrate your _____ .

7 Write a short message and invite your friend to your birthday party. Write what you would like to get and do.

1 **Read the blog. Why are Beret, Caterina, and Aurelio asking for advice?**

● ● ●

Help Your Health—Your Questions Answered!

Question: I know you shouldn't stay in the sun too long. I always put on sunscreen, but I still get sunburned. Any advice? —*Beret*

Answer: Don't forget to put on your sunscreen every hour and after swimming. You should also wear a T-shirt on the beach and you should drink a lot of water.

Question: I usually get the flu every winter. I always wear warm clothes but I still get sick. I feel very tired and I always want to sleep. What should I do? —*Caterina*

Answer: You should think about proper nutrition. Try to eat more fruit and vegetables on these cold days. You should also get lots of sleep and take some vitamins, too.

Question: I'm a mailman and I work very long hours. I often have backache and it's very painful. I sometimes take medicine, but it still hurts. Any advice? —*Aurelio*

Answer: You shouldn't take medicine very often without a doctor's permission. Try to find ways to relax. I think you should do some exercise to make your back stronger, too. How about yoga or Pilates?

2 **Read and write T (*true*) or F (*false*).**

1 Aurelio should do some exercise. ....

2 Caterina shouldn't take vitamins. ....

3 Aurelio shouldn't take medicine every day. ....

4 Beret should put on sunscreen after swimming. ....

3 **Read the blog and underline sentences with *should* and *shouldn't*.**

Grammar

He **should** eat more fruit in winter.

You **shouldn't** go to school when you're sick.

Should I take vitamins?

44

4 Match the questions to the answers.

1. I spent hours in front of the computer and now my eyes hurt. What should I do?
2. I ate too many fries and now I have a stomachache. What should I do?
3. I have a rash on my face and body. What should I do?
4. I have terrible toothache. What should I do?

A. You should go to the dentist.
B. You shouldn't eat anything else for a few hours but you should drink some water.
C. You should relax and keep away from computers for a while.
D. You should go and see a doctor.

5 Put the words in order.

1. to bed on You school days early should go

   ....

2. spend hours You on shouldn't the computer

   ....

6 Complete the sentences.

1. Megan has toothache. What should she do?

   Megan should ....

2. Samantha has a headache. What should she do?

   Samantha ....

3. Ethan has a fever. What should he do?

   He ....

7 Talk in pairs. Imagine you have a health problem. Ask your friend for some advice. Use the words in the box to help you.

a headache   a sore throat   toothache
a stomachache   backache   a fever

I have a fever. I think I have the flu. Should I eat some ice cream?

No, you shouldn't. You should go to the doctor and get some rest.

8 **Look at the pictures and read the questions. Write one-word answers.**

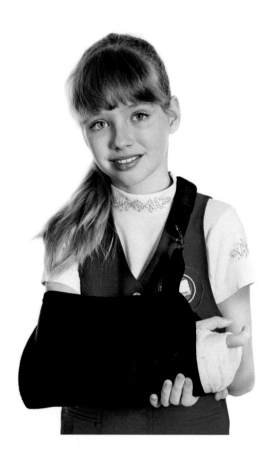 

The girl has broken her arm. What should she do?

She _____should_____ use her other arm.

1   What shouldn't she do?

    She _____ lift things with her broken arm.

2   What is wrong with Mr. Wilson?

    He hurt his _____ .

3   What should he do?

    He should get a lot of _____ .

4   What shouldn't he do?

    He shouldn't _____ heavy things.

You have to follow the rules!

1 **Read the dialog. Who has training on Saturdays?**

Lucas: Hi! I'm Lucas. Are you new?

Max: Hello! I'm Max. Yes, this is my first day at this school.

Lucas: I'm sure you will like it here, but you have to follow the rules.

Max: Can you tell me some of the school rules?

Lucas: Sure, the most important rule is you have to be at school on time.

Max: That won't be a problem for me. What else should I know?

Lucas: Secondly, you have to wear the correct school uniform every day.

Max: That's good to know.

Lucas: By the way, who is your teacher?

Max: Mrs. Rodriguez.

Lucas: She's great! But you have to do your homework on time

because she doesn't like late homework.

Max: Don't worry! I always do my homework on time.

Lucas: That's great!

Max: Do I have to come to school on Saturdays?

Lucas: No, you don't. Only the basketball team has training on Saturdays.

Max: How do I join the basketball team?

Lucas: You have to put your name on the list.

Max: Thanks for the information, Lucas! Good to meet you!

2 **Read and write T (*true*) or F (*false*).**

1 All students have to go to school on Saturday. ....

2 Lucas has to wear his school uniform every day. ....

3 He has to do his homework on time. ....

4 Lucas doesn't have to follow the school rules. ....

Grammar

You have to be at school on time.	You don't have to take the school bus.
Max has to wear his uniform.	He doesn't have to go to bed early.

Do I have to stay after school?	Yes, you do.	No, you don't.
Does he have to do homework?	Yes, he does.	No, he doesn't.

3 **Read the dialog again and underline sentences with *have to*.**

4 Circle the correct answer.

1 Miguel *have clean / has to clean* his room.

2 I *don't have / doesn't have* to do my homework tonight.

3 Yessica *having to / doesn't have to* go to bed early on the weekend.

4 Students *have to wearing / have to wear* their uniforms at school.

5 What is missing? Write.

1 I don't have .... wash the dishes at home.

2 She doesn't have .... wear a uniform at home.

6 Put the words in order.

1 bus   have   to   We   take   the   school   to   don't

....

2 have   uniform   to   school   wear   he   Does   every   day   a   to

.... ?

3 teacher   You   listen   to   the   to   have

....

4 have   tonight   do   her   to   chores   She   doesn't

....

7 Write about what you have to do and what you don't have to do. Use the phrases in the box to help you.

> help my brother/sister with homework   walk the dog
> be quiet during class   wear a school uniform   ~~do my homework~~
> study hard   take the bus to school   help with chores

I have to do my homework.

....

....

....

....

....

8 **Read the text. Choose a word from the box. Write the correct word next to numbers 1–5.**

A school uniform

Sometimes I'm a shirt and pants, or even a _____*skirt*_____ or a dress. I can be blue, **(1)** _____, black, or any other color. Students have to wear me at **(2)** _____ every day. I always have to be **(3)** _____ and never dirty. Children have to take me off when they go **(4)** _____ in the evening. They have to put me in their closets and put on their **(5)** _____ . What am I? A school uniform.

skirt

green

boots

clean

home

school

library

pajamas

1 Read the dialog. What are they bringing on the camping trip?

Carlos: Are you ready for the trip to the mountains?

Matthew: I'm almost ready. I'm trying to find my camera.

Carlos: We have to get everything ready tonight! What do we have ready so far?

Matthew: We have three water bottles, two tents, and a flashlight.

Carlos: What else do we need?

Lisa: We'll need one more tent, ropes, sleeping bags, and insect repellent.

Anna: I'll bring the tent. I have a big one at home.

Simon: My father has some rope in his garage. I'll bring it.

Matthew: How many sleeping bags do we need? Will you bring yours, Lisa?

Lisa: We need two more. I'll take mine and I'll ask my cousin if I can borrow hers.

Matthew: Will you call her now?

Lisa: No, I won't. I'll call her in the morning.

Matthew: Who will set up the tents? I can carry them, but I don't know how to set them up!

Simon: Don't worry. I'll help you.

Carlos: I'll buy some insect repellent tomorrow.

Matthew: I think everything is almost ready. See you all tomorrow at nine!

2 Who said this? Write the correct name.

1 I'll call her in the morning. ....

2 I'll bring the tent. ....

3 My father has some rope. ....

4 Who will set up the tents? ....

Grammar

I'll (will) bring the tents.	I won't help wash the dishes.
You'll (will) bring a flashlight.	You won't need the flashlight.
We'll (will) take a lot of pictures.	We won't be late.
Will you buy the insect repellent?	Yes, I will. No, I won't.

3 Read the dialog again and underline sentences with _will_, _'ll_, and _won't_.

4 **Match to make sentences.**

1	I'll	A	late. Hurry up!
2	Will	B	bring a cake.
3	You'll be	C	won't have the time.
4	We	D	you need a tent?

5 **Circle and write the correct letter.**

a o i

I w .... n't bring my camera. It was expensive.

6 **Put the words in order.**

1 carry will the tent You

....

2 tent sleep you Will in the

.... ?

3 bring the camera you Will

.... ?

4 wake up won't We early

....

7 **Think of a place you'd like to visit this summer. Answer the questions.**

Where will you go?

....

Who will you go with?

....

What will you take?

....

What will you do there?

....

8 Look at the pictures and read the story. Write some words to complete the sentences about the story. You can use 1, 2, or 3 words.

Maria and Alejandro went camping with their family on the weekend. They were very excited. Maria made a list of things they needed. "I will pack the sleeping bags and a flashlight," said Maria. "Will you put the tent in the car, Alejandro? It's so heavy, I can't carry it." Alejandro thought that his sister was bossy.

Maria and Alejandro were ___excited about___ *going camping.*

1 Maria _____ the sleeping bags and a flashlight.

2 Alejandro thought Maria was _____ .

The children put some warm clothes and their hiking boots in their backpacks. "I will pack the insect repellent," said Mom. "There are a lot of bugs at the campsite." "Can I take my bike? I'd like to ride it at the campsite," asked Alejandro.

3 Mom will pack _____ .

4 Alejandro would like to _____ around the campsite.

Everyone was ready to go. "This will be the best camping trip ever," said Alejandro. They got in the car and Dad started to drive. They arrived at the campsite in the afternoon. Maria and Alejandro helped Mom unpack everything. Dad set up the tents. Maria wanted to take some pictures with her new camera, but she couldn't find it. "You didn't put your camera on the list," said Alejandro.

5 _____ drove the car.

6 They _____ at the campsite in the afternoon.

7 Maria forgot to bring _____ .

1 Read the text. What's Olympus Mons?

Some people believe that our generation is the luckiest. Scientists say that space tourism will be possible over the next 40 years. Scientists have been working on spaceships for many years. Many believe they'll be ready in this century, within our lifetime. Some people say that flying to other planets in the solar system will happen by 2050.

The spaceships will carry tourists to amazing places, such as the Moon and even the Red Planet (Mars). But it won't be possible to travel to other galaxies for a few more generations.

Scientists predict that the first astronauts will go to Mars by 2030. There will be small crews of only four to six people in the beginning. First, they'll explore the surface of Mars, then they'll visit Olympus Mons, the tallest volcano in the solar system. One day, it will also be possible to live on Mars within a special space colony!

But will space travel really be possible for everyone one day? I'm sure it will. The only problem is it will be very expensive. So, you should start saving up now!

2 Read and write *Yes* or *No*.

1 The first missions will go to Jupiter. ....

2 The spaceships will carry tourists to the Sun. ....

3 It won't be possible to travel to other galaxies for a long time. ....

4 Flights to space will be very expensive. ....

3 Read the text again and underline *will*, *'ll*, and *won't*.

4 Match to make sentences.

1 People will fly   A cost a lot of money to visit space.

2 It will   B will explore the surface of Mars.

3 Astronauts   C to Mars in 2050.

Grammar

He/She/It'll explore Mars.	He/She/It won't travel to space.	
They'll need a lot of money to travel in space.	They won't live on Mars because it's too expensive.	
Will he live in a colony on Mars?	Yes, he will.	No, he won't.
Will they walk on the Moon?	Yes, they will.	No, they won't.

5 💡 Put the words in order.

1 be | cheap | Space | travel | won't

....

2 fly | to | they | other | Will | planets

.... ?

3 will | crews | be | The | small

....

6 Look at the pictures and complete the sentences with the correct form of the verbs.

1 Scott .... (fly) in a spaceship one day. He's training to be an astronaut.

2 Astronauts .... (not/explore) Mars this year.

Journey to Mars

VIEW INFO

Solar System Exploration

VIEW INFO

3 Tourists .... (travel) to other planets one day.

4 Space tourists .... (have to) pay a lot of money, because space travel .... (not/be) cheap!

7 💬 Talk with a friend about what our world will be like in 2050. Use the phrases in the box to help you.

> flying cars   intelligent robots   cities on other planets
> computerized glasses   high-tech smartphones
> self-driving trucks   travel to the Sun

People will have flying cars in the future.

I think we won't have intelligent robots in 2050. Building them will take more time.

8  **Read the text and choose the best answer.**

Marcos   Hi Seren! What are you reading?

Seren   A   OK. I'm tired now.

*   (B)   I found this article about people living on Mars.*

*   C   I like listening to music.*

1   Marcos: Do people live there?

Seren: A   No, but they will in about 40 years.

            B   It will carry tourists.

            C   I haven't got one.

2   Marcos: Will it be expensive to go there?

Seren: A   No, I can't.

            B   Yes, it will.

            C   Yes, I'm very good at it.

3   Marcos: How will people get there from Earth?

Seren: A   He doesn't know how to fly.

            B   It should walk.

            C   They will fly in a spaceship.

4   Marcos: How many people will be able to fly in the spaceship?

Seren: A   It will only carry four to six people.

            B   They can't fly because they're too young.

            C   She will be 12 on her next birthday.

5   Marcos: Will people also travel to the Moon?

Seren: A   It's bigger than the Earth.

            B   No, they don't.

            C   Yes, I think so.

6   Marcos: Let's go to space together one day!

Seren: A   That's a great idea!

            B   He wasn't with me.

            C   Yes, of course I can.

1 **Read the text. Why is it important to eat fruit and vegetables?**

We would all like to eat cookies, a bag of chips, ice cream, or bar of chocolate. These things are sometimes called "junk food". But why aren't they healthy? It's because they are lower in nutrition than fruit and vegetables and full of empty calories. We have to eat a lot of fruit and vegetables every day so we can be healthy. Fruit and vegetables are rich in vitamins and minerals. The more you eat, the healthier and more energized you will feel.

Doctors say we should eat one to four cups of vegetables each day. They provide many important nutrients, like potassium, fiber, and vitamins A, E, and C.

We should also eat one to two cups of fruit each day. Fruit is rich in vitamin C and vitamin A. An orange a day will build your immune system and this will protect you from getting colds in winter.

Exercising is also important because it keeps our bodies fit and healthy. Sports like tennis, basketball, and gymnastics are a fun and exciting way to exercise. So the best way to stay fit and healthy is by eating healthy food and playing a lot of sports!

2 **Read and write T (*true*) or F (*false*).**

1 Fruit is rich in vitamins C and D. ....

2 We should eat fruit every day. ....

3 Playing sports is good for our bodies. ....

4 Cookies, chips, ice cream, and chocolate are healthy. ....

3 **Read and underline sentences with *will*, *have to*, *because*, and *would like*.**

4 **Match to make sentences.**

1 I would like

2 By playing sports, you will

3 An orange

4 We have to

5 Junk food isn't healthy

A eat healthy food and do a lot of exercise.

B will give you a lot of vitamin C.

C have a fit and healthy body.

D because it isn't rich in vitamins.

E to drink a cup of water.

5 Answer the questions. Use the phrases in the box.

> it's raining   swimming is my favorite sport
> I have to do my homework
> my best friend forgot my birthday

1 Why are you going to the library?

I'm going to the library because ....

2 Why are you sad?

I'm sad ....

3 Why are you carrying your umbrella?

I'm carrying it ....

4 Why do you like summer?

I like summer ....

6 Look at the pictures and complete the sentences.

1 What would you like to eat?

I .... like to eat a .... of chips.

2 What would you like to drink?

I would .... to drink some ....

3 What .... ?

I .... to eat a .... of chocolate.

4 .... ?

....

7 Talk with a friend about what places you would like to visit on vacation. Use the words in the box to help you.

> beach   campsite   mountains   country

Where would you like to go?

First, I think I'll visit the beach because I love swimming. Then...

8 **Read the text. Choose the right words and write them on the lines.**

Hello. My name's Sandra. I ___will___ be ten years old next month. I usually get up early and drink a **(1)** _____ of orange juice. I eat a **(2)** _____ of bread with peanut butter and jelly every morning. I leave for school every morning at 8:00. There are a lot of rules at my school, but the most important is that we have **(3)** _____ wear our uniform every day. I love my English teacher, Mrs. Nolan, very much. Sometimes she gives us extra homework **(4)** _____ we are too noisy during the lesson. This week, we were very noisy, so I'm sure we **(5)** _____ have a lot of homework this weekend.

	(will)	am	do
1	bowl	glass	bag
2	bar	cup	slice
3	by	to	in
4	because	so	why
5	will	are	didn't

1 **Read the texts. Who won the Artist of the Year award?**

Matias Acosta

Matias Acosta was a professional soccer player. He played for some of the best clubs around the world. He played as a forward and he was the team captain for Brazil. He won the Player of the Year award in 2010. He's a coach now.

Carolina de Angelica

Carolina de Angelica is one of the most successful actresses in the world. She won an award for best actress in 2001. She is well known for her beautiful voice. She does a lot of charity work. She helps poor people in Asia and Africa and children around the world.

Jack Sun

Jack Sun is a very popular Canadian singer and songwriter. He was born in Toronto. He released his first album in 2007 and won the Artist of the Year award in 2008. He is popular with young people, but he has a lot of older fans as well. He supports many international charities. They build schools and hospitals in developing countries.

2 **Read and write T (*true*) or F (*false*).**

1 Matias plays for a Swedish soccer team. ....

2 Matias never won the Player of the Year award. ....

3 Carolina de Angelica is a famous dancer. ....

4 Jack Sun supports charities. ....

3 **Read the text again and underline sentences that talk about the past.**

4 **Circle the correct answer.**

1 Kelly *study / studies* Spanish at school.

2 Sarah and Jane often *go / goes* to the movie theater.

3 Simon *go / went* to Madrid two years ago.

4 Helen and I don't *swim / swam* in the lake in winter.

5 Put the words in order. You have to change some words.

1 sing   I   public   never   in

....

2 movie   last   act   a   year   in   She

....

3 summer   Mexico   go   He   every   to

....

4 milk   drink   I   breakfast   yesterday   for

....

6 Complete the sentences with the correct form of the action words.

> go   do   visit   swim   go   ride

Every summer

1 Amanda .... to the beach.

2 She .... in the ocean.

3 She .... homework because there's no school!

Last year

1 Amanda .... to London.

2 She .... Big Ben and the Tower of London.

3 She .... the London Eye because the line was too long!

7 Write about your favorite singer, actor, actress, or sports star. Write about why he or she is famous and what he or she did in the past.

My favorite .... is ....

He/She ....

In the past, he/she ....

....

....

....

....

8 **Read the text and choose the best answer.**

Julio: Hi, Elena. What are you doing?

Elena: A   I'm not going to.

(B)   I'm reading an article about my favorite singer.

C   Yes! Thanks.

1   **Julio:**   Who is your favorite singer?

Elena: A   I like Jenifer Lee Cortez. She is very good.

B   I don't like to sing.

C   Jenifer Lee Cortez isn't my favorite.

2   **Julio:**   Is she famous?

Elena: A   She's a very good singer.

B   Yes, people all over the world know her music.

C   She is from Canada.

3   **Julio:**   Does she act, too?

Elena: A   My sister is an actress, too.

B   She worked at a movie theater when she was young.

C   She acted in a movie last year.

4   **Julio:**   Which sports star do you like?

Elena: A   I usually play tennis with my friend Kim.

B   I played basketball last week.

C   I like Lucy Tang. She won a gold medal at the Olympics.

5   **Julio:**   Do you like movies?

Elena: A   I don't have a favorite actor.

B   Yes, I like watching movies on the weekend.

C   I went to a big concert last weekend.

6   **Julio:**   What TV shows did you watch this weekend?

Elena: A   I went to the swimming pool.

B   I watched a documentary about space.

C   I like watching TV.

Irregular Verbs List

Infinitive	Past Simple
be	was/were
begin	began
blow	blew
break	broke
bring	brought
build	built
buy	bought
can	could
choose	chose
come	came
cost	cost
cut	cut
do	did
draw	drew
drink	drank
drive	drove
eat	ate
fall	fell
feel	felt
fight	fought
find	found
fly	flew
get	got
give	gave
go	went
grow	grew
have	had
hear	heard
hold	held
keep	kept
know	knew
lay	laid
lead	led

Infinitive	Past Simple
leave	left
let	let
lie	lay
lose	lost
make	made
mean	meant
meet	met
pay	paid
put	put
read	read
ring	rang
run	ran
say	said
see	saw
sell	sold
send	sent
set	set
sing	sang
sit	sat
sleep	slept
speak	spoke
spend	spent
stand	stood
take	took
teach	taught
tell	told
think	thought
understand	understood
wake	woke
wear	wore
win	won
write	wrote

arson Education Limited

) Two

) Park

low

ex

17 9NA

gland

d Associated Companies throughout the world.

w.English.com

st published 2019

hth impression 2022

3N: 978-1-292-21946-2

: in Daytona Pro Primary 12/16pt

nted and bound by CPI Group (UK) Ltd, Croydon CR0 4YY

knowledgements

e review sections were written by Chris Speck.

e publisher would like to thank the following for their kind permission to
roduce their photographs:

ey: b-bottom; c-centre; l-left; r-right; t-top)

3RF.com: 13, 21 (tiger), 35bl, 43/1, 43/4, 49 (green), 50, 53, 54b, 56,
nunna1 27, dacasdo 38/4, evdoha 37/1, kankhem 19b, marinaabcd 8,
znyakov 46l, pressmaster 6c, sergeydv 54c, stockyimages 59b, Tom Wang 37/4,
vebreakmediamicro 15; **Pearson Education Ltd:** Studio 8 14, 58, 40tc, Jon
rlow 43/2, Sophie Bluy 32t, Gareth Boden 29, Handan Erek 49 (library), Arvind
gh Negi / Red Reef Design Studio. Pearson India Education Services Pvt. Ltd
t, MindStudio 38/2, Tudor Photography 17b, 40tr, Rafal Trubisz. Pearson Central
rope SP. Z.O.O. 47, Jules Selmes 7, 55; **Shutterstock.com:** 37/3, 40bl, 41b, 43/3,
(boots), 49 (skirt), 52t, 54t, 57/2, 57/3, arek_malang 32 (chocolates), Arnoud
anjer 34c, ArtFamily 38/5, Atthapol Saita 35tc, blessings 20c, Brian A Jackson
, Brocreative 37/2, Canon Boy 4, davegkugler 23br, Debbie Aird Photography 23cr,
nis Radovanovic 40br, dibrova 16, Dmussman 34b, Dragon Images 9, dragon_fang
r, EcoPrint 21 (giraffe), Elena Yakusheva 17c, ElenaGaak 32 (cake), Eric Isselee
bc, Ethan Daniels 23cl, FikMik 40bc, Franck Boston 49 (pajamas), Freek Frederix
b, Gemenacom 38/1, GorillaAttack 32 (milk), Hung Chung Chih 23tr, 35tl, Hurst
oto 17t, Ian Maton 21 (bear), Inc 6t, Jacek Chabraszewski 26, James Laurie
bl, Johan_R 21 (crocodile), Kruglov_Orda 35br, Lance Bellers 40tl, Lightspring
t, Mats 32 (crisps), Matt Jeppson 23tl, Melanie DeFazio 49 (school), Monkey
siness Images 11, 18, 24, 52c, Morgan Lane Photography 31, nattanan726 22,
ypong 34t, New beginnings 19tr, ollyy 59t, parinyabinsuk 20b, Patrick Foto 5,
21 (whale), romakoma 49 (home), Skynavin 21 (snake), SnowWhiteimages 44,
ephane Angue 35tr, Steve Cukrov 57/4, stockshoppe 32 (can), Subbotina Anna 49
ean), Syda Productions 61, tanik 19tl, Tund 57/1, Vasilyev Alexandr 38/3, Yuganov
nstantin 59c

other images © Pearson Education

ver photo © **Getty Images:** Hero Images

ustrated by Chiara Fiorentino (Astound US) 7, 29.

known reuse artists: 8, 19, 41